MENSA CHESS

Rosalyn B. Katz, Fred Wilson & Bruce Alberston

**OFFICIAL MENSA
PUZZLE BOOK**

Main Street

A division of Sterling Publishing Co., Inc.
New York

Library of Congress Cataloging-in-Publication Data Available

2 4 6 8 10 9 7 5 3 1

This book is excerpted from the following Sterling titles:
Start Playing Chess, by Rosalyn B. Katz originally published in Great Britain &
© 1993 under the title *Chess for Children* by Collins & Brown Limited and
Cadogan Books Limited. Text © 1993 by Rosalyn B. Katz
303 Tactical Chess Puzzles, written by Fred Wilson & Bruce Alberston
© 2002 by Fred Wilson & Bruce Alberston

Published by Sterling Publishing Co., Inc.
387 Park Avenue South, New York, NY 10016
© 2004 by Sterling Publishing Co., Inc.
Distributed in Canada by Sterling Publishing

^C/o Canadian Manda Group, One Atlantic Avenue, Suite 105
Toronto, Ontario, Canada M6K 3E7
Distributed in Great Britain and Europe by Chris Lloyd at Orca Book
Services, Stanley House, Fleets Lane, Poole BH15 3AJ, England
Distributed in Australia by Capricorn Link (Australia) Pty. Ltd.
P.O. Box 704, Windsor, NSW 2756, Australia

Printed in United States of America
All rights reserved

ISBN 1-4027-1639-7

CONTENTS

STARTING CHESS

1. THE GAME

To play chess you must think and plan.
BRAIN POWER is the key to winning.

There are two players, known as White (who moves the white pieces) and Black (who moves the black pieces). Each player wants to capture the other's King.

Important Things to Know

- Each piece occupies one square. The pieces can move to different squares, but can only take an enemy square by capturing the piece that's on it.

- Check—attack the enemy King.

- Checkmate (or mate)—attack the enemy King so that it cannot escape.

- Capture—bump an enemy piece off the board by moving your piece onto its square.

- Move—each player gets a turn to move one piece at a time. (Except when castling—but we'll talk about that later.) The player with the white pieces gets to move first.

To play you need a board and pieces.

The object of the game is to checkmate the enemy King. "Mate" it—so it can't escape.

Check

You are in check when your King is attacked by an enemy piece. You must get out of check right away.

Ways to get out of check

- Block—put another piece in the way
- Capture—take away the enemy piece
- Move—put the King on a safe square

Checkmate

When a King is in check and has no way to get out of check, the game is over. Checkmate or "mate."

Stalemate/Draw

When there are no remaining legal moves on the board and neither King is in check, it is stalemate. Nobody wins—it's a draw.

It's also a draw if...

the same position is repeated three times during the game with the same player to move each time;

or

there are not enough pieces to mate;

or

both players agree to a draw.

Resignation

When a player has a horrible position, with no way to win or draw, that player may resign. That also means the game is over.

Sometimes players agree to a draw—and go play tennis,

or start another game.

A chess game starts when White makes the first move and ends when:

White wins (Score: 1–0)

Black wins (Score: 0–1)

Draw (Score: ½–½)

2. THE BOARD

The Board is the world of the chess pieces.

The chess board has light and dark squares.

A light square is always on the bottom right corner.

Light on Right.

Each square on the board has a name with a number and a letter.

The numbers go up the side.

The letters go across the bottom.

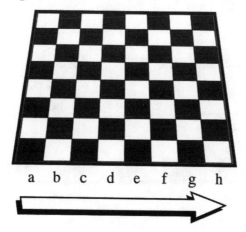

To find d6, go right to d, and up to 6.

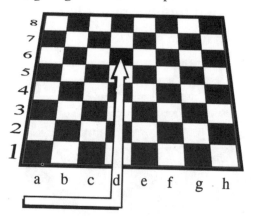

Each row on the chess board is called a rank. The row numbered 7 is called the 7th rank.

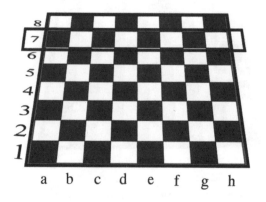

Each column of a chess board is called a file. The "a" file is the left-most file on the board.

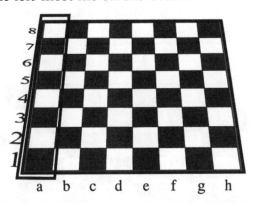

Put a ✓ on square e5.

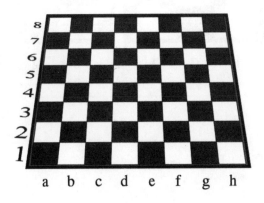

Did you find e5?

If you found e5, go to the next chapter to learn about the pieces. If you did not find e5, go back to page 11 and read it again.

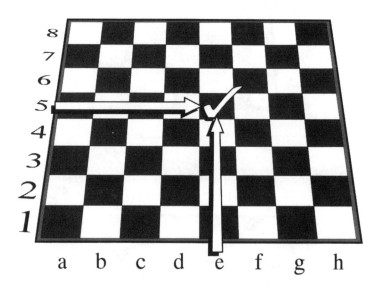

3. The Pieces

NAME	SYMBOL	LETTER
Knight		N
Rook		R
Bishop		B
Queen		Q
King		K
Pawn		a, b, c, d, e, f, g, h

The pieces always start on the same squares (see the following page).

The pawn is known by the letter of its file.

Each piece has a different job and makes different moves.

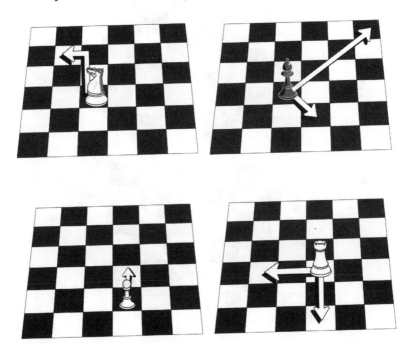

You are the boss of all your pieces like a conductor telling musicians how to play, or a coach managing a team.

When your pieces work together to protect your King and to beat the enemy, you win.

Some pieces have more power than others.		
Piece		**Value in Pawns**
Q ♕	9	♟♟♟♟♟♟♟♟♟
R ♖	5	♟♟♟♟♟
B ♗	3	♟♟♟
N ♘	3	♟♟♟

THE KNIGHT

N

The Knight starts on these squares.

b1 and g1 for White

b8 and g8 for Black

The Knight is the only piece that can jump over other pieces. It moves two squares in one direction, and one square in another direction.

This Knight can go to a3 or c3 or d2.

The Knight always winds up on a different-color square from where it started.

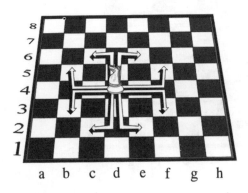

The arrow shows all the squares that the Knight on d4 can move to.

A Knight in the middle of the board has eight possible moves.

This Knight can move from c4 to d2. Two squares down and one square right.

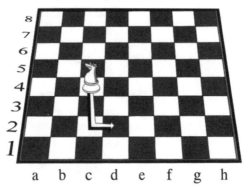

The Knight can also move from c4 to b6. Two squares up and one square left.

The Knight can also move from c4 to b2. Two squares down and one square left.

The Knight attacks any piece that is on a square that it can move to. To capture an opponent's piece, the Knight replaces the opponent's piece. The captured piece is taken off the board.

The Knight on c4 can capture any of these pieces.

A) Put an "N" on each square where the Knight on e6 can move.

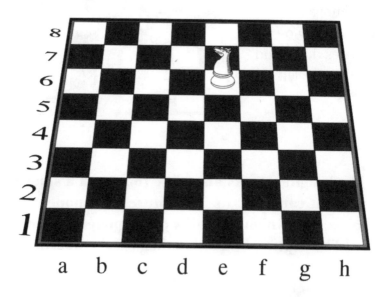

B) Put X's on all pieces that can be captured by the black Knight on e7.

A) Did you find all the "Ns?"

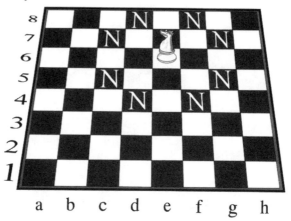

B) Did you remember that the Knight can jump over pieces and it captures only enemy pieces?

THE ROOK

R

The Rooks start on these squares.

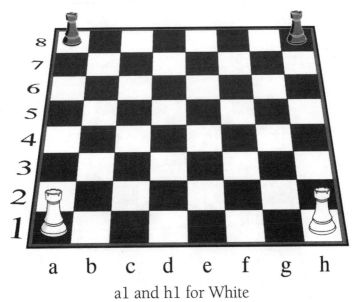

a1 and h1 for White

a8 and h8 for Black

The Rook moves straight up, down, or sideways any number of squares: a1 to h1 or a1 to a8. Like this.

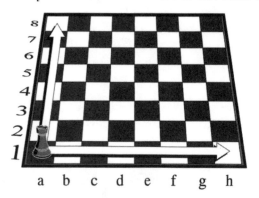

Or this.

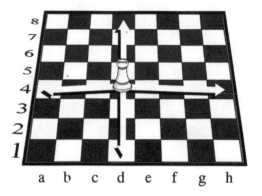

The Rook attacks any piece directly in its path. The Rook captures the same way as it moves. The Rook cannot jump over another piece. It stops before it hits the other piece, or it captures the enemy piece. When it is moved to a square that contains an opponent's piece, it replaces that piece and the piece is removed from the board.

Here it can capture the Queen or the Pawn or the Knight or the Bishop.

A) Put an "R" on all the squares the c5 Rook can go.

B) Put an "X" on all pieces that the Rook on e4 can capture.

A) Did you find all the "R" squares?

B) Did you mark the Bishop on e6?

THE BISHOP

B

The Bishops start on these squares.

c1 and f1 for White

c8 and f8 for Black

The Bishop moves diagonally. It cannot move straight up and down or sideways; it moves diagonally, always on the same-color square. Like this.

c1 to a3 or c1 to h6 or any squares along the way.

Remember, it cannot jump over another piece. Only the Knight can do that.

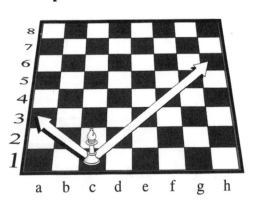

Or this.

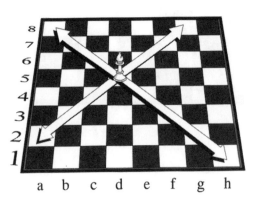

It stays on the same color for the whole game. The "light" Bishop must always land on a light square. The "dark" Bishop must always land on a dark square.

The Bishop attacks any piece in its path. The Bishop captures the same way it moves. When it captures the enemy piece, it takes over its square.

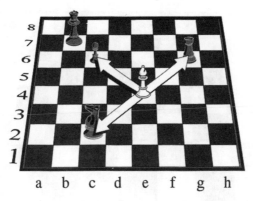

A) Put a "B" on every square the e5 Bishop can go to.

B) Which pieces can the White Bishop capture?

A) Did you find all the "B" squares?

B) Did you remember that the Bishop cannot jump over pieces but can capture an enemy piece?

The Queen

Q

The Queens start on d1 for White and d8 for Black.

The White Queen starts on a light square.

The Black Queen starts on a dark square.

The Queen is the strongest piece on the board.
It can move like a Bishop or a Rook.
Like this:

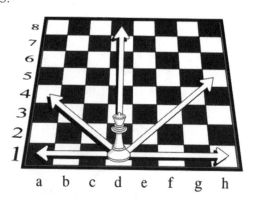

Or this:

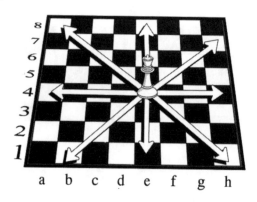

The Queen attacks any piece directly in its path.

The Queen captures the same way that it moves.

The Queen cannot jump over other pieces.

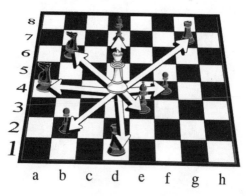

A) Put a "Q" on all the squares the d4 Queen can go.

B) Which pieces can the White Queen capture?

A) Did you find all the "Q" squares?

B)

THE PAWN

P

The pawns start across the second rank for White and across the seventh rank for Black.

Pawns move only forward, never backward. The pawn moves straight ahead, one square at a time—except on its first move or when it captures a piece.

Pawns do strange things.

Pawns:

- can move one or two squares on their first move
- turn into other pieces when they get all the way across the board
- move forward but capture diagonally
- change their names after capturing
- pretend the enemy pawn moved one square instead of two in the special *"en passant"* move

When the pawn first moves, it goes one or two squares.

The e-pawn goes to e3 or e4.

The pawn is named for the file that it's on (a, b, c, d, e, f, g, or h). After its first move, a pawn can move only one square at a time.

Put an "e" on all the squares this pawn can move to.

Did you find e3 and e4?

A pawn attacks a piece when that piece is one square diagonally ahead of it. When a pawn captures an enemy piece, it moves diagonally one square—replacing the piece it captures.

The e-pawn captures the d-pawn on d5.

A pawn cannot capture the piece on the square directly in front of it.

**Put an "X" on all the pieces that
can be captured by the e-pawn.**

Good, if you marked the Knight on f3.

When a pawn is successful in moving all the way to the other end of a file it turns into a Queen (or any other piece you pick except a King).

EN PASSANT

Capturing *"en passant"* (in passing) happens only with pawns.

If a pawn on its start square moves two squares landing next to an enemy pawn, it can be captured as if it moved only one square. The capture must happen right away.

The Black d-pawn captures the White c-pawn on c3.

THE KING

K

The Kings start on e1 for White and e8 for Black.

They face each other across the board.

**You have to take really good care of your King.
It is *the most important* piece in chess.**

The King moves only one square at a time, but can move in any direction.

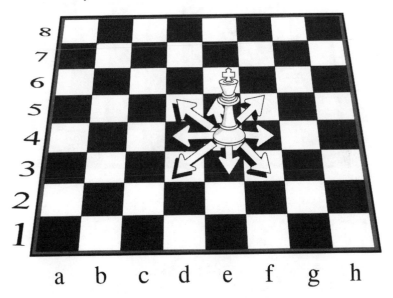

It can not move to a square where it will be in check.

The King can capture a piece on any square that is next to it, as long as the King will not be in check.

Put a "K" on all the squares this c3 King can go.

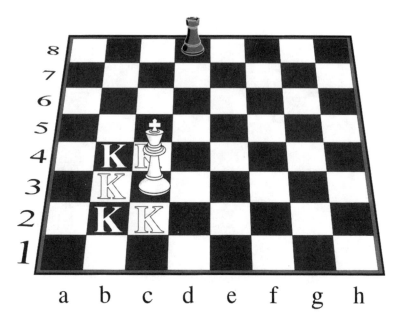

**Did you find all the "K" squares?
The King could not move to the "d" file
because it would be in check.**

Put an "X" on the pieces the White King can capture.

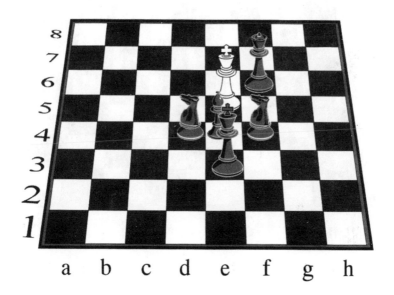

**Only the Black Queen! The other Black pieces
are protected. The White King can't capture
them because it would be in check.**

CASTLING

Castling is the only time two pieces move at once—the King and Rook.

It is the only time a King moves more than one square and the only time a Rook jumps over a King.

You can NOT castle if:

- the King is in check
- the King or Rook has been moved earlier in the game
- other pieces are in the way
- the King must pass through check on any of the squares

To castle Kingside.

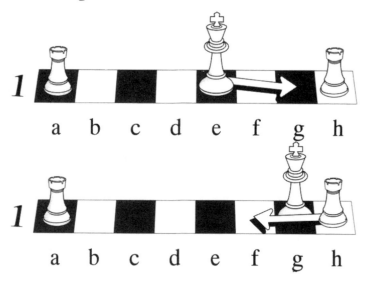

It looks like this.

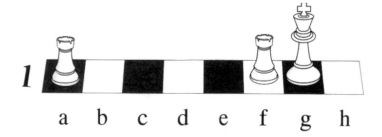

To castle Queenside.

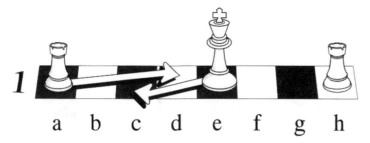

It looks like this.

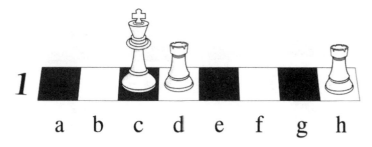

Remember: Move the King two squares toward the Rook and put the Rook on the other side of the King.

A) Castle Kingside (shown by O—O) by putting a K and R to show the castled position below.

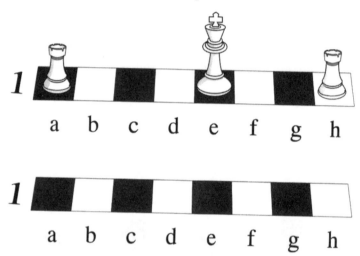

B) Now castle Queenside (O—O—O).

A) O—O

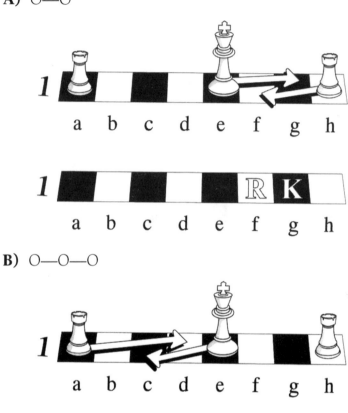

B) O—O—O

4. MATES AND ATTACKS

Here are some simple positions for you to look at. Since you need to "mate" to win, this chapter will help you set up winning positions. Write on the pages to show where the pieces go. Draw an arrow to show how you're moving a piece. You turn the page to find the best answer.

A good idea is to use a board and pieces to work out the problems.

In the diagram above, White moves.
Find how White mates in one move.

A)

White moves. Find how White mates in one.

B)

White moves. Find how White mates in one move.

A)

B)

A)

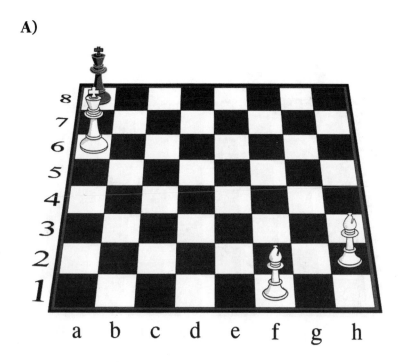

Black to move—what happens now?

B)

White moves. Find the mate.

A)

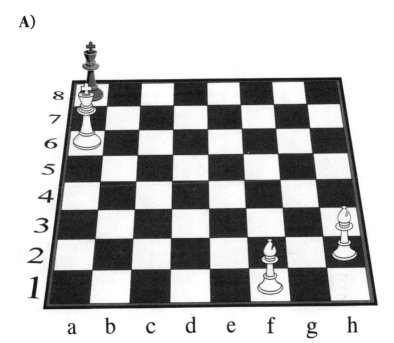

If it is Black to move, it's a draw. Black has no legal move and is stalemated.

B)

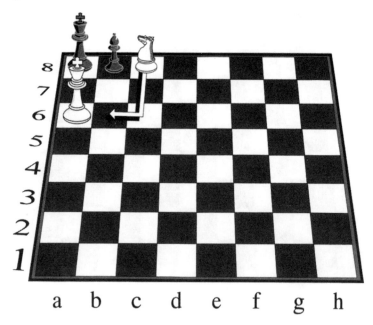

A)

White moves. Find how White mates in one move.

B)

If White moves, what is best?

A)

The c-pawn promotes to a Knight, instead of the usual Queen. A Knight would "mate" the Black King.

B)

Now Black's King is in check. When the King moves the Bishop can capture the Queen.

A)

What is the best move for Black?

B)

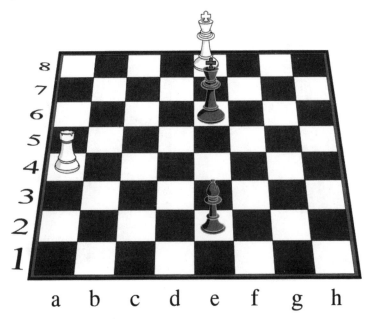

Black moves. What is the best move?

A)

Black will capture the Queen.

B)

Now White's King is in check.

When the King moves the Bishop can capture the Rook.

White moves. What's the best move?

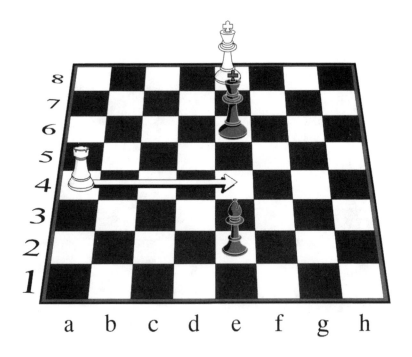

Now Black's King is in check. When the King moves the Rook can capture the Bishop.

5. WRITING THE GAMES

This section teaches you how to keep a record of the moves. You can get a score book to write the moves, or just write them on a piece of paper. You write your games so that you can:

- go over them
- learn from your mistakes
- show them off!!!

To write or read games, you need to know the letters and symbols used.

The Pieces

WRITE	MEANING
K	King
Q	Queen
R	Rook
B	Bishop
N	Knight
a, b, c, d, e, f, g, h	Pawn

The Moves

SYMBOL	MEANING
X	captures
+	check
++	checkmate
!	good move
!!	great move
?	bad move
??	rotten move
?!	may be bad
!?	interesting
0–0	castles Kingside
0–0–0	castles Queenside

Reading the moves.

...c5

This means that Black (...) moved the c-pawn to c5.

exf6

This means that the e-pawn (White) captured on f6.

O—O—O

This means White castled Queenside.

...Qf2++

This means Black's Queen to f2 checkmate.

Write the moves shown by the arrows for A and B.

A)

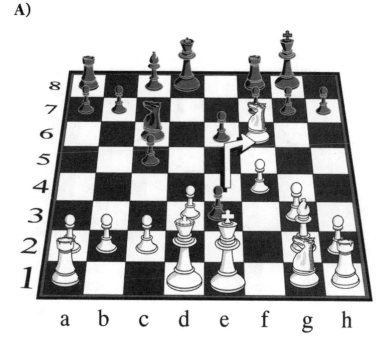

There was a Black Bishop on f6 above.

B)

Is this how you wrote the moves?

A)

Nxf6+

B)

...O—O

Write the moves shown by the arrows for both A and B.

A)

B)

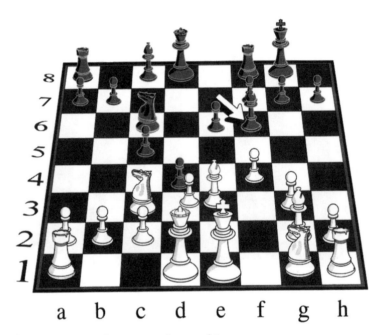

There was a White Knight on f6.

Is this how you wrote the moves?

A)

Rb1

B)

...Bxf6

6. GETTING STARTED

Remember:

- White always starts.
- Protect your King.
- Look for good moves that get your pieces attacking.

Set your board to play your own game.

Which pieces can move on the first move?

Put a "**✓**" on all the pieces White can move to start
the game.

Did you mark all the pieces?

Now "✔" all the pieces that Black can move.

All the pawns or the Knights can move on the first turn.

7. A REAL GAME

Many players look at other people's games to get good ideas. You can find games in newspapers, chess books, and chess magazines. The game in this section will give you practice in reading chess notation, and in playing through a complete game.

Use your board and chess set to play through this game, move by move. Playing it through will show you how to:

- develop pieces
- move pieces during a game
- capture pieces
- "trap" enemy pieces and the enemy King
- "mate"

The game was played September 9, 1992, at the Morris County Chess Club in New Jersey.

White was Bill Petersen. Black was Roz Katz.

Move 1.e4

1 ...c5

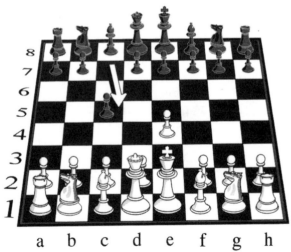

	White	Black
1	e4	c5
2	Nc3	Nc6
3	g3	Nf6
4	Bg2	e6
5	d3	Be7
6	Be3	0-0
7	f4	d5
8	e5	d4!!
9	exf6	Bxf6
10	Ne4	dxe3
11	Nxf6+	Qxf6
12	Bxc6!?	bxc6
13	Rb1	e5
14	fxe5??	Qf2++

2. Nc3

2 ...Nc6

	White	Black
1	e4	c5
2	Nc3	Nc6
3	g3	Nf6
4	Bg2	e6
5	d3	Be7
6	Be3	0-0
7	f4	d5
8	e5	d4!!
9	exf6	Bxf6
10	Ne4	dxe3
11	Nxf6+	Qxf6
12	Bxc6!?	bxc6
13	Rb1	e5
14	fxe5??	Qf2++

3. g3

3 …Nf6

	White	Black
1	e4	c5
2	Nc3	Nc6
3	g3	Nf6
4	Bg2	e6
5	d3	Be7
6	Be3	0-0
7	f4	d5
8	e5	d4!!
9	exf6	Bxf6
10	Ne4	dxe3
11	Nxf6+	Qxf6
12	Bxc6!?	bxc6
13	Rb1	e5
14	fxe5??	Qf2++

4. Bg2

4 ...e6

	White	Black
1	e4	c5
2	Nc3	Nc6
3	g3	Nf6
4	Bg2	e6
5	d3	Be7
6	Be3	0-0
7	f4	d5
8	e5	d4!!
9	exf6	Bxf6
10	Ne4	dxe3
11	Nxf6+	Qxf6
12	Bxc6!?	bxc6
13	Rb1	e5
14	fxe5??	Qf2++

5. d3

5 ...Be7

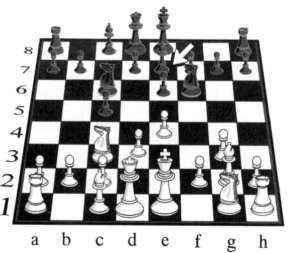

	White	Black
1	e4	c5
2	Nc3	Nc6
3	g3	Nf6
4	Bg2	e6
5	d3	Be7
6	Be3	0-0
7	f4	d5
8	e5	d4!!
9	exf6	Bxf6
10	Ne4	dxe3
11	Nxf6+	Qxf6
12	Bxc6!?	bxc6
13	Rb1	e5
14	fxe5??	Qf2++

6. Be3

6 ...0-0

	White	Black
1	e4	c5
2	Nc3	Nc6
3	g3	Nf6
4	Bg2	e6
5	d3	Be7
6	Be3	0-0
7	f4	d5
8	e5	d4!!
9	exf6	Bxf6
10	Ne4	dxe3
11	Nxf6+	Qxf6
12	Bxc6!?	bxc6
13	Rb1	e5
14	fxe5??	Qf2++

7. f4

7 ...d5

	White	Black
1	e4	c5
2	Nc3	Nc6
3	g3	Nf6
4	Bg2	e6
5	d3	Be7
6	Be3	0-0
7	f4	d5
8	e5	d4!!
9	exf6	Bxf6
10	Ne4	dxe3
11	Nxf6+	Qxf6
12	Bxc6!?	bxc6
13	Rb1	e5
14	fxe5??	Qf2++

8. e5

8 ...d4!!

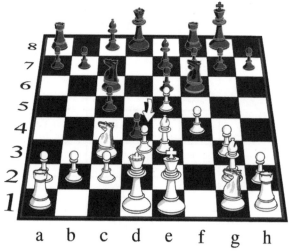

	White	Black
1	e4	c5
2	Nc3	Nc6
3	g3	Nf6
4	Bg2	e6
5	d3	Be7
6	Be3	0-0
7	f4	d5
8	e5	d4!!
9	exf6	Bxf6
10	Ne4	dxe3
11	Nxf6+	Qxf6
12	Bxc6!?	bxc6
13	Rb1	e5
14	fxe5??	Qf2++

9. exf6

9 …Bxf6

	White	Black
1	e4	c5
2	Nc3	Nc6
3	g3	Nf6
4	Bg2	e6
5	d3	Be7
6	Be3	0-0
7	f4	d5
8	e5	d4!!
9	exf6	Bxf6
10	Ne4	dxe3
11	Nxf6+	Qxf6
12	Bxc6!?	bxc6
13	Rb1	e5
14	fxe5??	Qf2++

10. Ne4

10 ...dxe3

	White	Black
1	e4	c5
2	Nc3	Nc6
3	g3	Nf6
4	Bg2	e6
5	d3	Be7
6	Be3	0-0
7	f4	d5
8	e5	d4!!
9	exf6	Bxf6
10	Ne4	dxe3
11	Nxf6+	Qxf6
12	Bxc6!?	bxc6
13	Rb1	e5
14	fxe5??	Qf2++

11. Nxf6+

11 ...Qxf6

	White	Black
1	e4	c5
2	Nc3	Nc6
3	g3	Nf6
4	Bg2	e6
5	d3	Be7
6	Be3	0-0
7	f4	d5
8	e5	d4!!
9	exf6	Bxf6
10	Ne4	dxe3
11	Nxf6+	Qxf6
12	Bxc6!?	bxc6
13	Rb1	e5
14	fxe5??	Qf2++

12. Bxc6!?

12 …bxc6

	White	Black
1	e4	c5
2	Nc3	Nc6
3	g3	Nf6
4	Bg2	e6
5	d3	Be7
6	Be3	0-0
7	f4	d5
8	e5	d4!!
9	exf6	Bxf6
10	Ne4	dxe3
11	Nxf6+	Qxf6
12	Bxc6!?	bxc6
13	Rb1	e5
14	fxe5??	Qf2++

13. Rb1

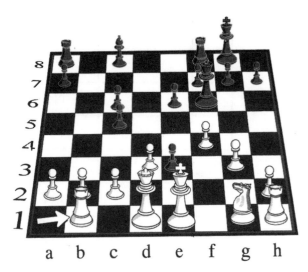

13 ...e5

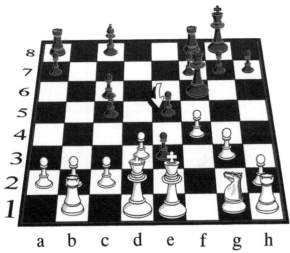

	White	Black
1	e4	c5
2	Nc3	Nc6
3	g3	Nf6
4	Bg2	e6
5	d3	Be7
6	Be3	0-0
7	f4	d5
8	e5	d4!!
9	exf6	Bxf6
10	Ne4	dxe3
11	Nxf6+	Qxf6
12	Bxc6!?	bxc6
13	Rb1	e5
14	fxe5??	Qf2++

14. fxe5??

14 ...Qf2++

	White	Black
1	e4	c5
2	Nc3	Nc6
3	g3	Nf6
4	Bg2	e6
5	d3	Be7
6	Be3	0-0
7	f4	d5
8	e5	d4!!
9	exf6	Bxf6
10	Ne4	dxe3
11	Nxf6+	Qxf6
12	Bxc6!?	bxc6
13	Rb1	e5
14	fxe5??	Qf2++

8. PLAYING TIPS

1. Get your pieces out fast!

2. Castle to make your King safe.

3. Learn how to DRAW a game.

4. Move your King after most pieces are off the board. The King is strong in the endgame.

5. Think about your move. Don't move too fast.

6. **Guess the other player's move.**

7. **Write down your moves.**

8. **Get other players to look at your games.**

9. **Join a chess club, or start one.**

10. **Be brave. Don't be afraid to make a risky move.**

11. **Have fun!!**

CHESS PUZZLERS

INTRODUCTION

Chess is the gymnasium of the mind.

—Adolf Anderssen

*Almost all games between inexperienced players
are decided by a tactical blunder, usually
the loss of at least a full piece.*

—Bruce Alberston

We want you to make this section your chess workout place. Whenever you have the time, or need to do some mental stretching before a serious game, we want you to enter our tactical chess "gym" here, and solve and solve until you really feel good and sharp.

We have, between us, nearly fifty years of practical chess teaching experience and if there is one thing we have learned for sure it is that the only way for the advanced beginner or intermediate player to improve to the next level is to keep studying tactics.

While chess is clearly a strategic game, 99% of the time your success or failure will be determined by your skill at tactics. So it's simple: You've got to study tactics or you'll never get any better....Get going!

—Fred Wilson & Bruce Alberston

100 POSITIONS FOR THE ADVANCED BEGINNER

The Advanced Beginner: Just who is the advanced beginner? Well, you happen to be your average chessplayer. You're thoroughly conversant with the moves and rules, and you've had some limited exposure to the basic concepts of the opening, middlegame, and ending. What you lack is the experience to put everything together into a coherent whole. What you also lack is the tactical ability to lift your game to a higher plane. Hopefully, these puzzles will help remedy this particular deficiency.

Anyway, the problems in this chapter are geared to the level of our hypothetical average advanced beginner. You're expected to solve the majority of the positions (over 50%), but we also expect you to do some stretching. The stretching is important if you want to move up a class in strength.

Scoring: Scoring is optional, but if you want to keep track, here's how to do it. There are a hundred positions in the chapter, each one worth one point. Give yourself full credit if you worked out the main line of the solution. And if you found only the first move, you can still give yourself a half-point part credit. As for the two bonus positions at the end of the chapter, don't worry if you miss them, but take credit if you solve them and add on to your score.

We would also like to see intermediate and tournament players trying their hand at this chapter. The chart below shows the average expected score for each category of player.

Player category	Average number of postions correctly solved, out of 100	Average number of postions incorrectly solved, out of 100
Advanced Beginner	64	36
Intermediate Player	76	24
Tournament Player	92	8

1.

White to move
(Pin)

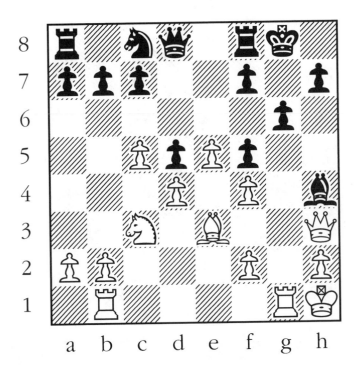

2.

White to move
(Trapping)

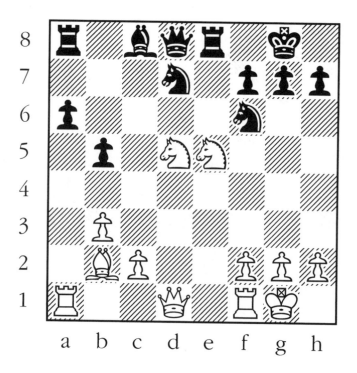

3.

White to move
(Pin)

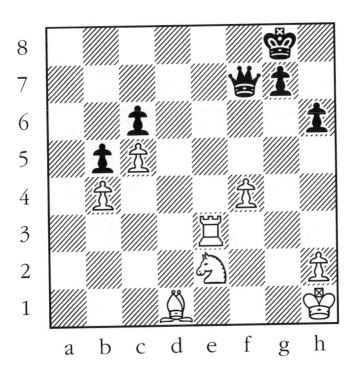

4.

Black to move
(Queen fork)

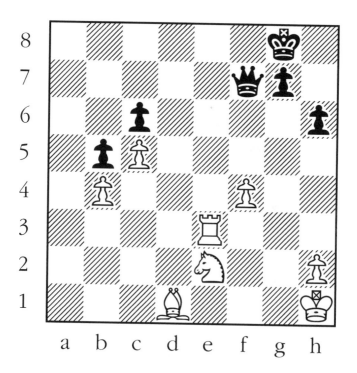

5.

White to move
(Pin)

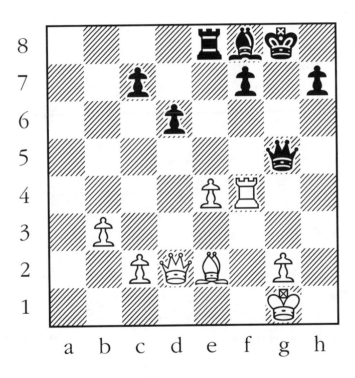

6.

Black to move
(Pin)

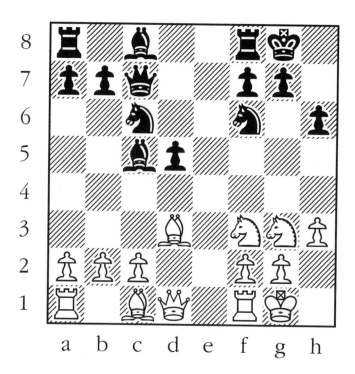

7.

Black to move
(Trapping)

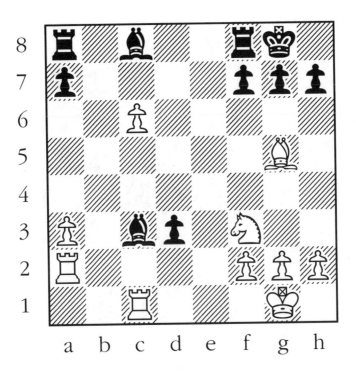

8.

White to move
(Double threat)

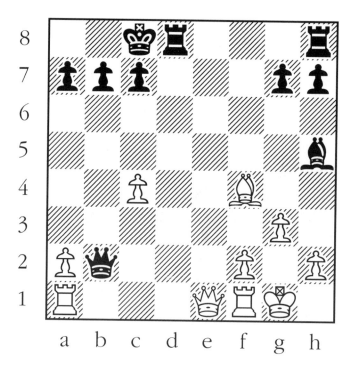

9.

White to move
(Trapping)

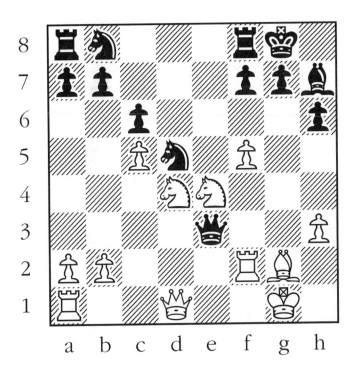

10.

Black to move
(Double threat)

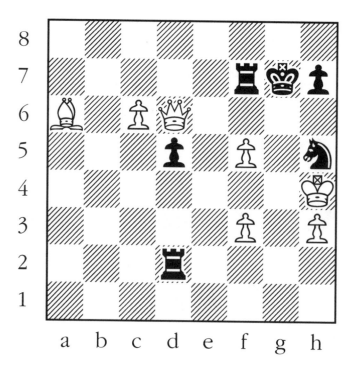

11.

White to move
(Removing the guard)

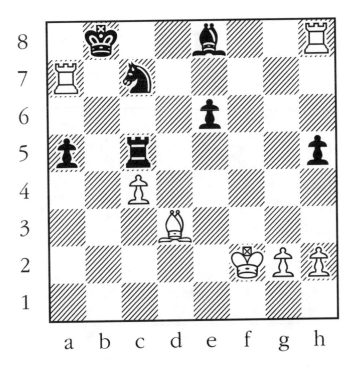

12.

White to move
(Removing the guard)

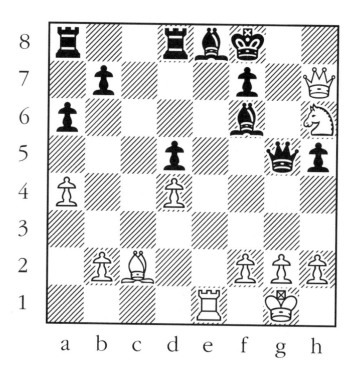

13.

Black to move
(Double threat)

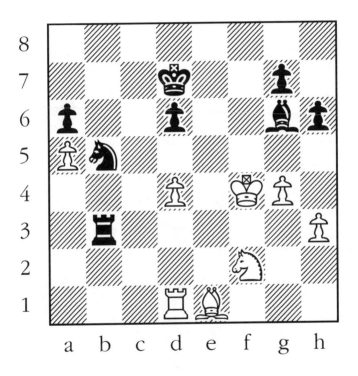

14.

Black to move
(Stalemate)

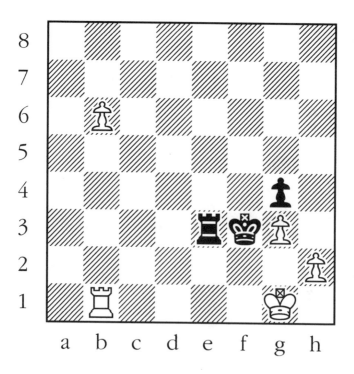

15.

Black to move
(Trapping)

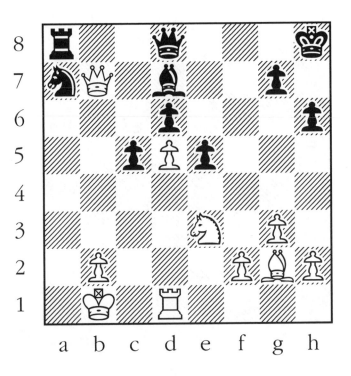

16.

Black to move
(Stalemate)

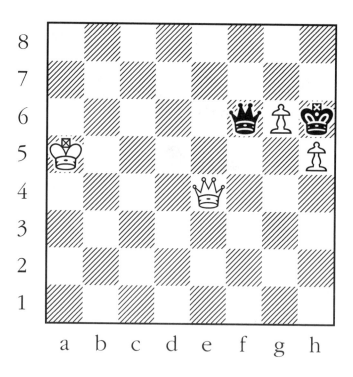

17.

White to move
(Removing the guard)

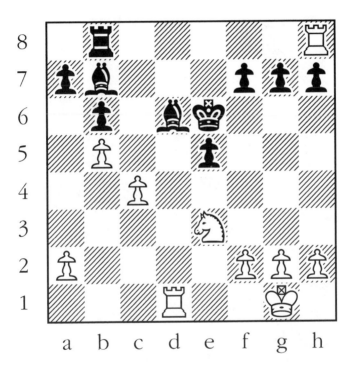

18.

White to move
(Mating attack)

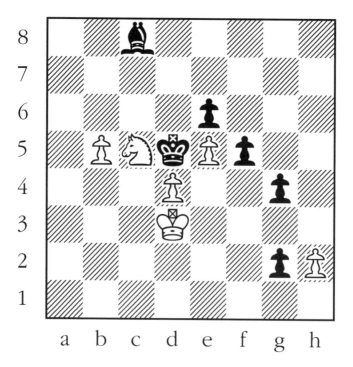

19.

Black to move
(Stalemate)

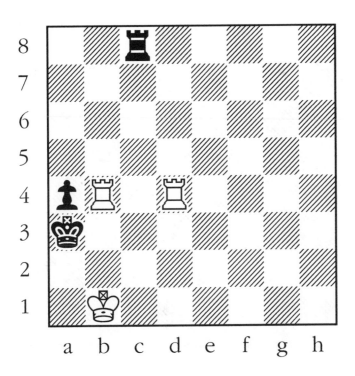

20.

White to move
(Pin)

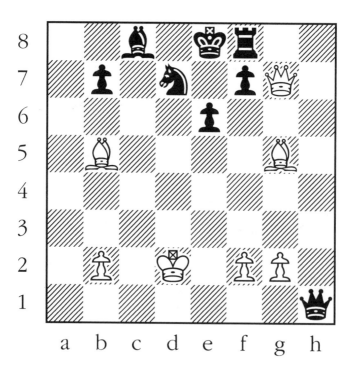

21.
Black to move
(Discovery)

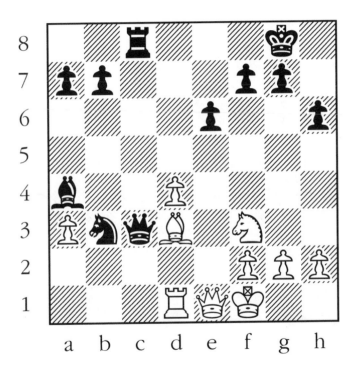

22.
White to move
(Discovery)

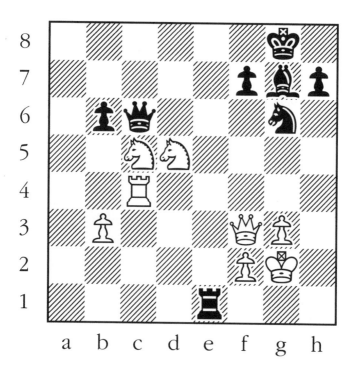

23.

White to move
(Removing the guard)

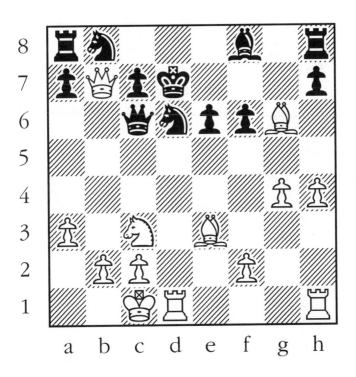

24.

Black to move
(Bishop fork)

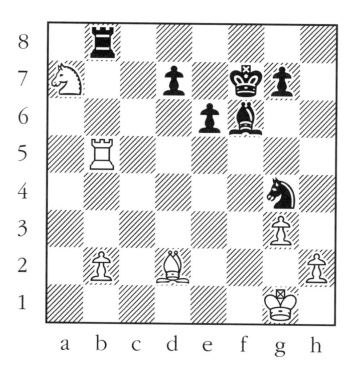

25.

White to move
(Trapping)

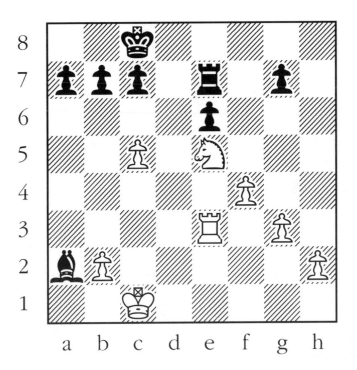

26.

White to move
(Removing the guard)

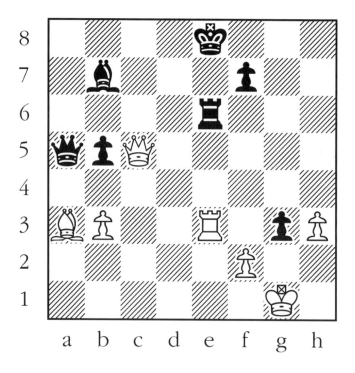

27.

White to move
(Simplification)

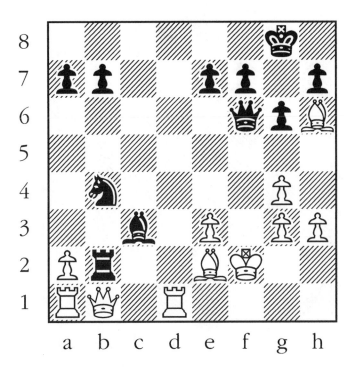

28.

Black to move
(Simplification)

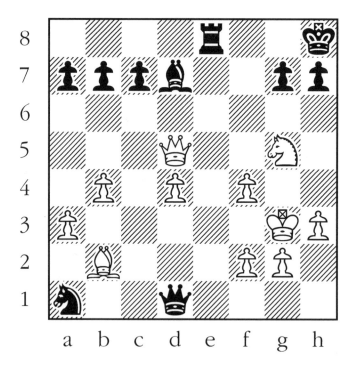

29.

Black to move
(Deflection)

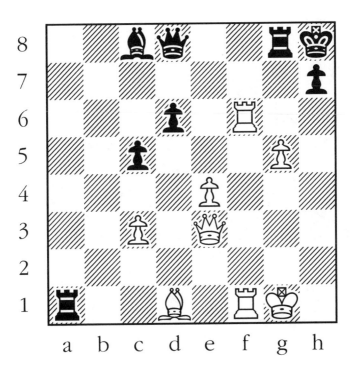

30.
Black to move
(Pin)

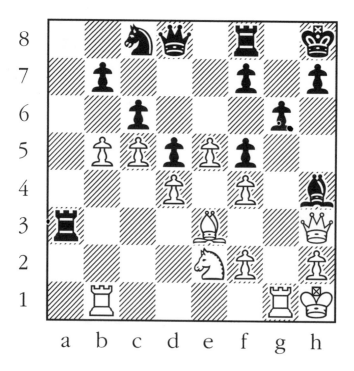

31.

White to move
(Overload)

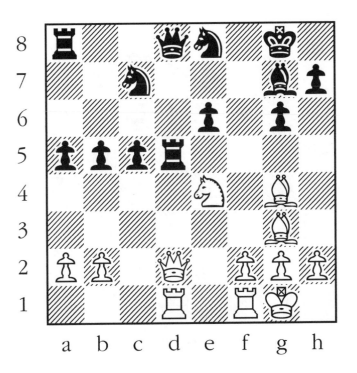

32.

White to move
(Trapping)

33.

Black to move
(Desperado)

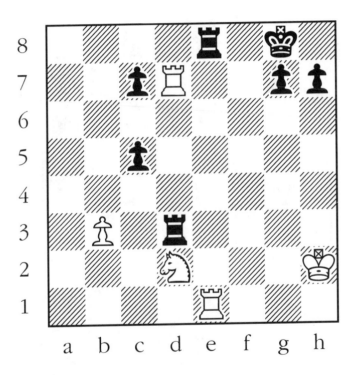

34.

White to move
(Removing the guard)

35.

Black to move
(Trapping)

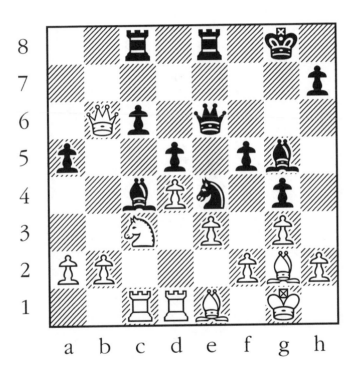

36.

Black to move
(Knight fork)

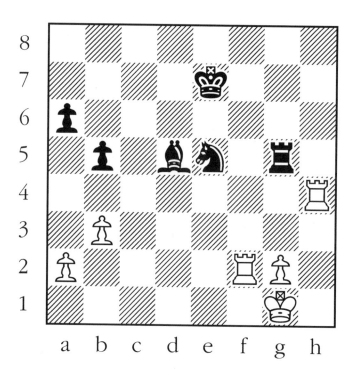

37.

White to move
(Mating attack)

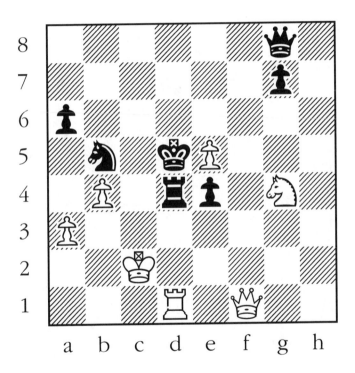

38.

White to move
(Overload)

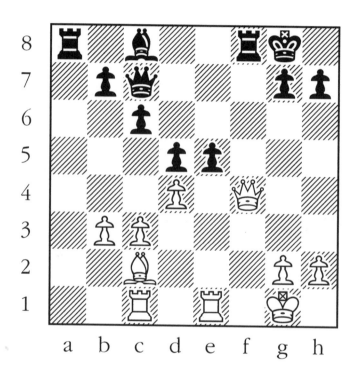

39.

White to move
(Driving off)

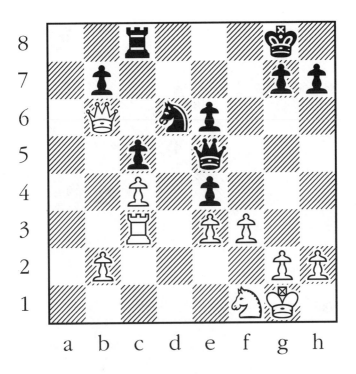

40.

Black to move
(Knight fork)

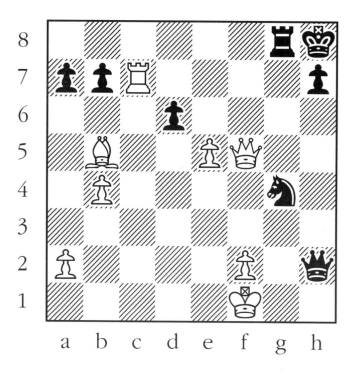

41.

Black to move
(Overload)

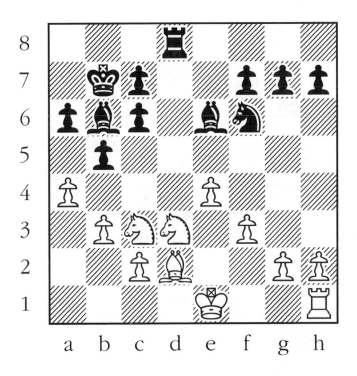

42.

White to move
(Driving off)

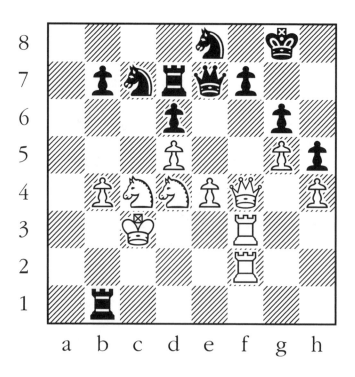

43.

White to move
(Pin)

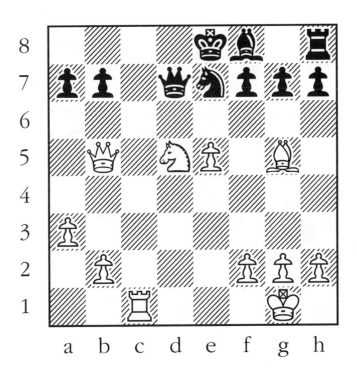

44.

White to move
(Knight fork)

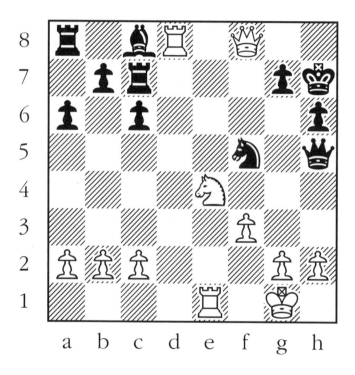

45.

Black to move
(Mating attack)

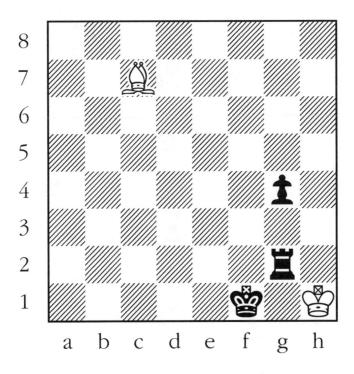

46.

White to move
(Overload)

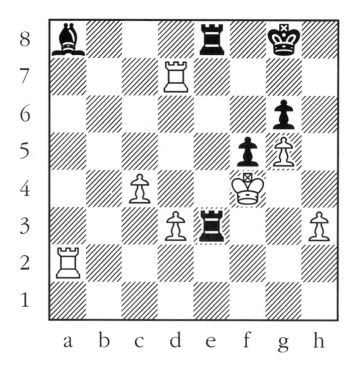

47.
Black to move
(Double check)

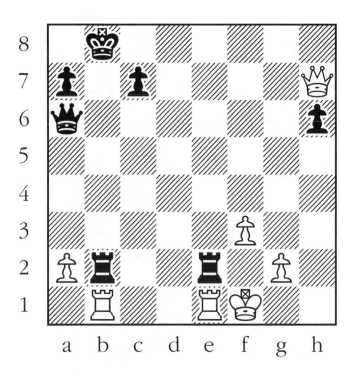

48.

White to move
(Trapping)

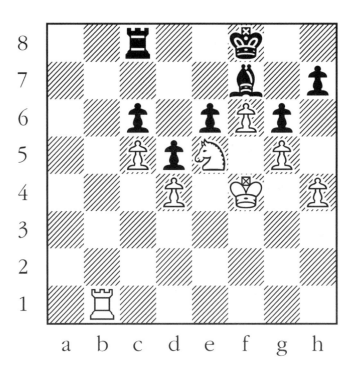

49.

White to move
(Knight fork)

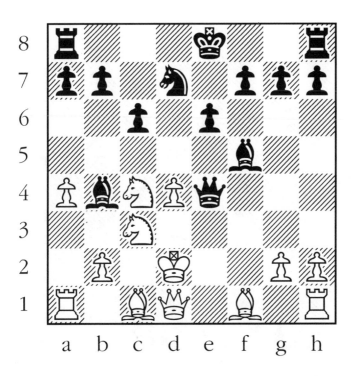

50.

White to move
(Discovery)

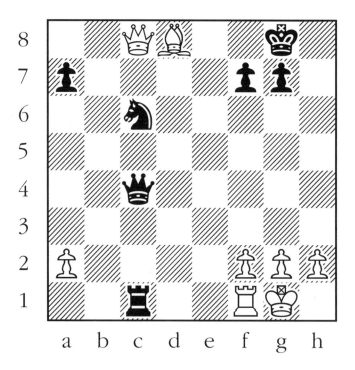

51.

White to move
(Removing the guard)

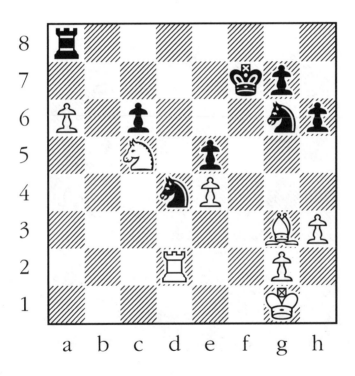

52.
Black to move
(Deflection)

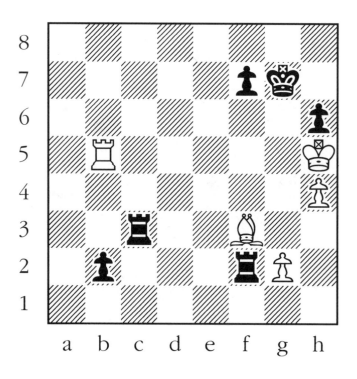

53.

Black to move
(Knight fork)

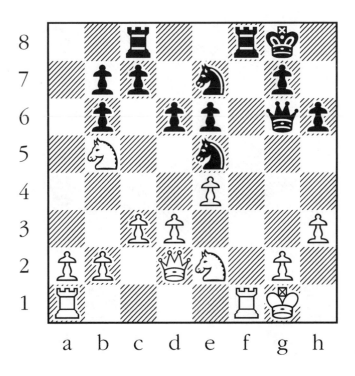

54.

Black to move
(Mating attack)

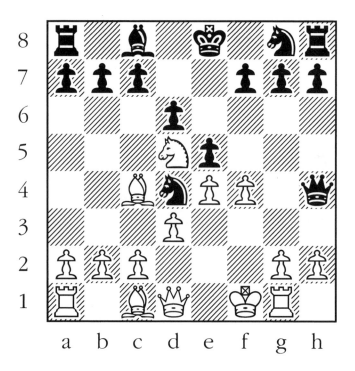

55.

White to move
(Knight fork)

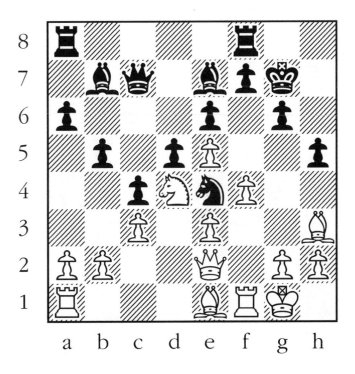

56.

White to move
(Promotion)

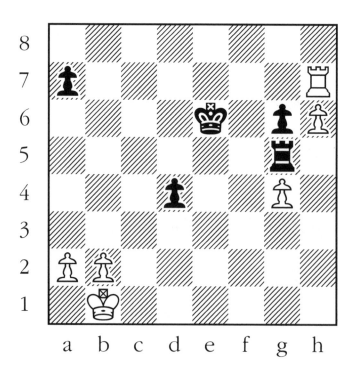

57.
White to move
(Trapping)

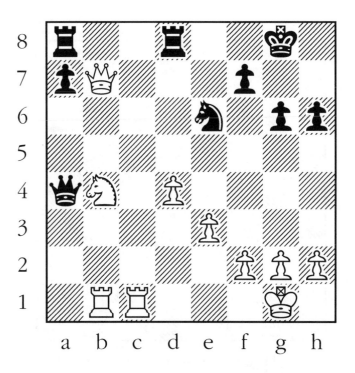

58.

White to move
(Discovery)

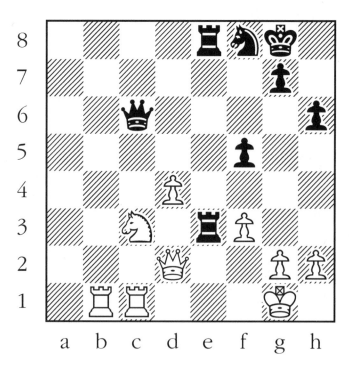

59.

White to move
(Promotion)

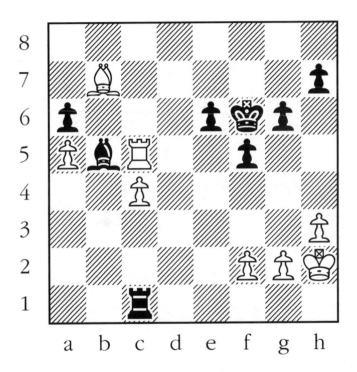

60.
White to move
(Pin)

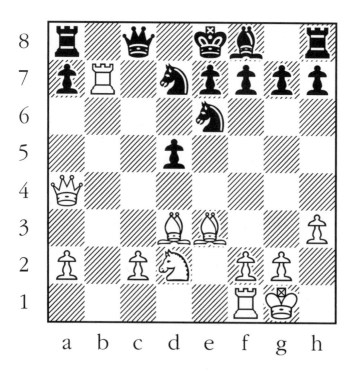

61.

Black to move
(Removing the guard)

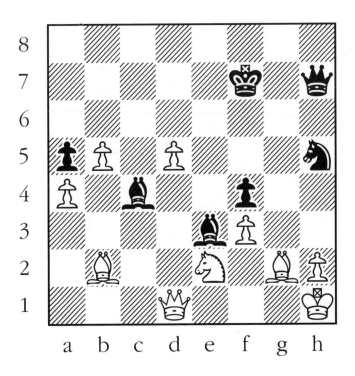

62.

Black to move
(Removing the guard)

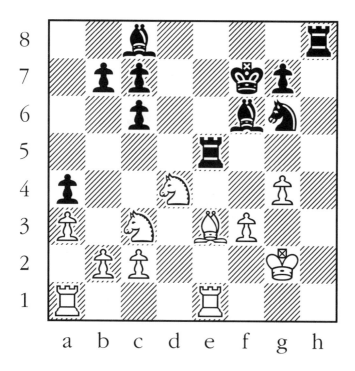

63.

White to move
(Mating attack)

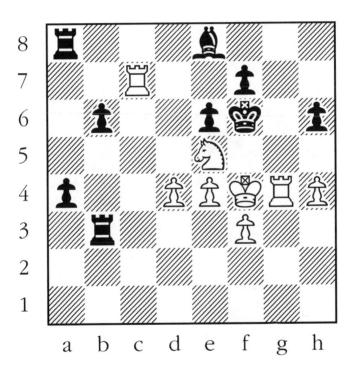

64.

White to move
(Mating attack)

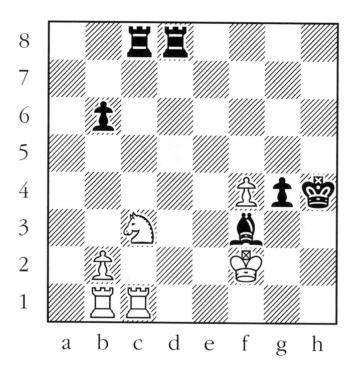

65.

White to move
(Mating attack)

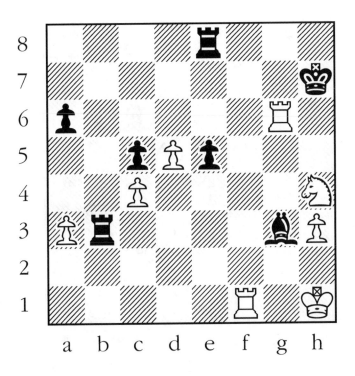

66.
Black to move
(Trapping)

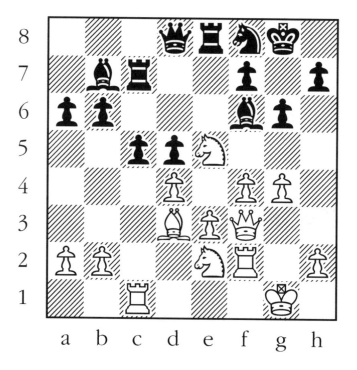

67.
White to move
(Deflection)

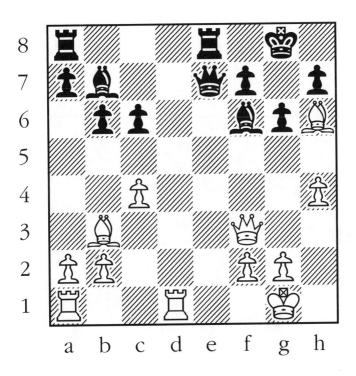

68.

White to move
(Mating attack)

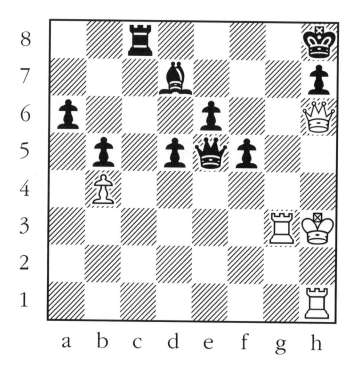

69.

White to move
(Overload)

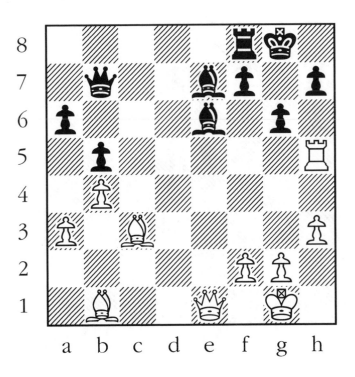

70.

White to move
(Discovery)

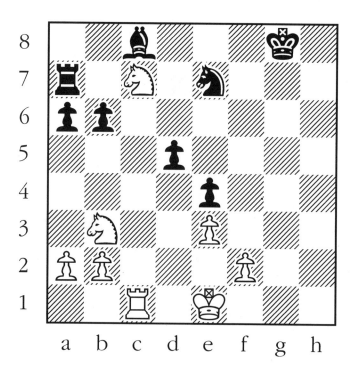

71.

White to move
(Deflection)

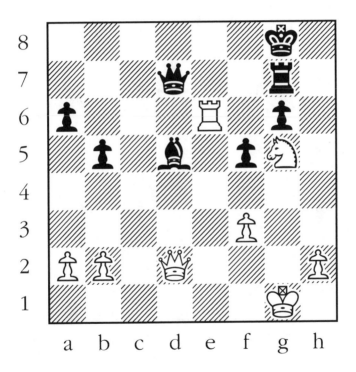

72.

White to move
(Removing the guard)

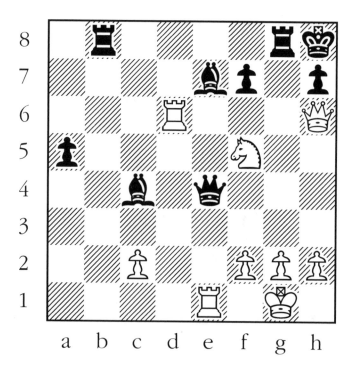

73.
White to move
(Pin)

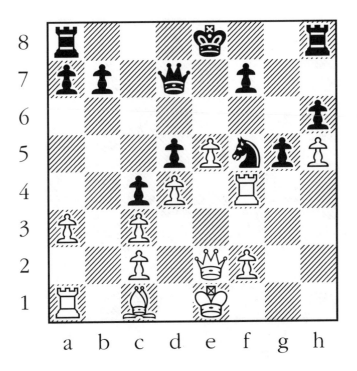

74.

Black to move
(Mating attack)

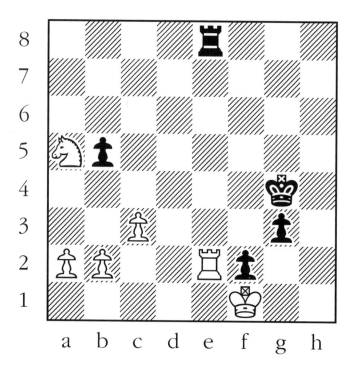

75.

White to move
(Interference)

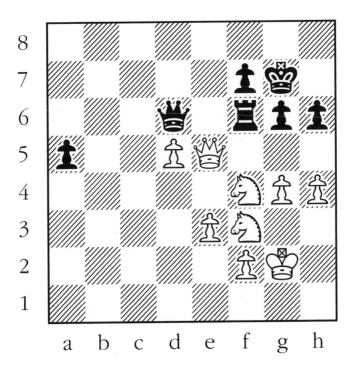

76.
Black to move
(Pin)

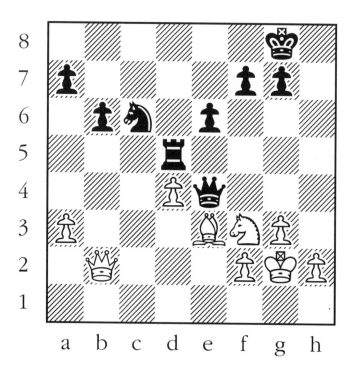

77.
Black to move
(Removing the guard)

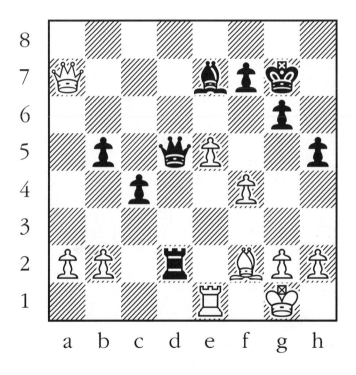

78.

Black to move
(Pin)

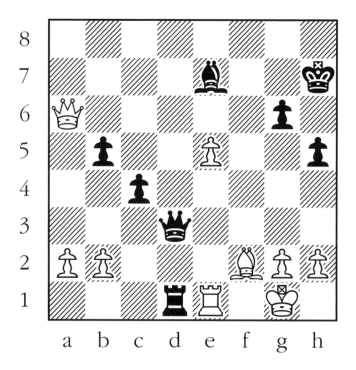

79.
White to move
(Deflection)

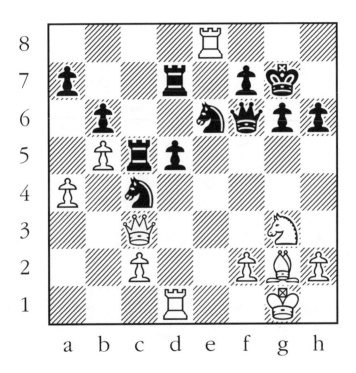

80.

White to move
(Discovery)

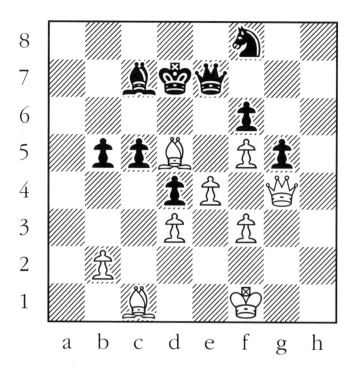

81.
White to move
(Pin)

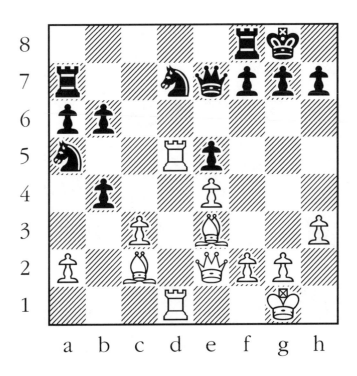

82.
White to move
(Pin)

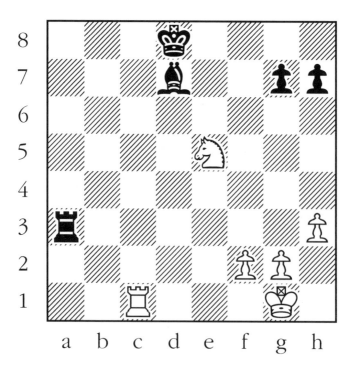

83.
White to move
(Deflection)

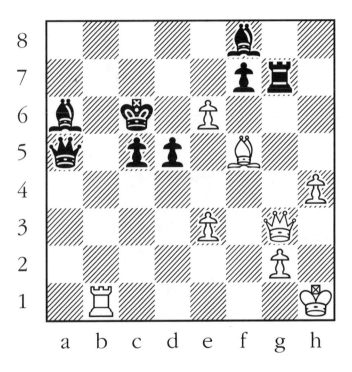

84.

White to move
(Removing the guard)

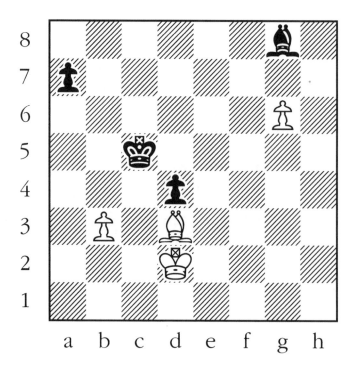

85.
White to move
(Pin)

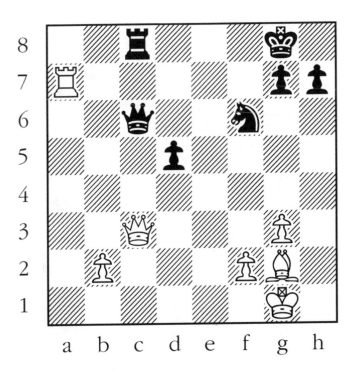

86.

White to move
(Promotion)

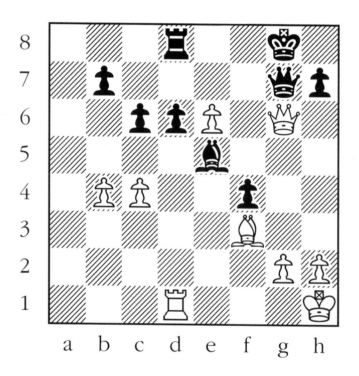

87.
Black to move
(Deflection)

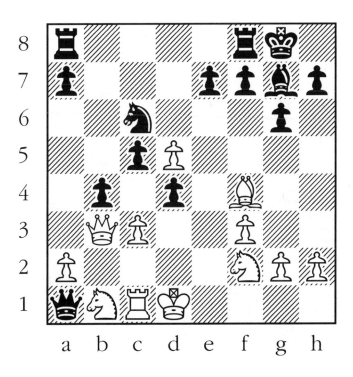

88.

Black to move
(Trapping)

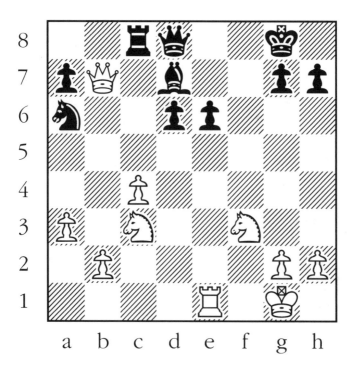

89.

White to move
(Removing the guard)

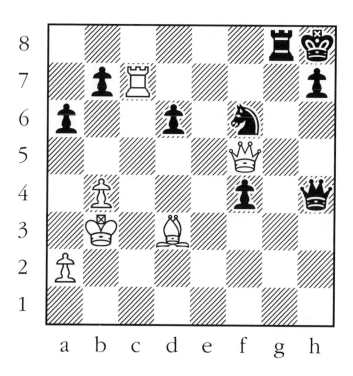

90.

White to move
(Knight fork)

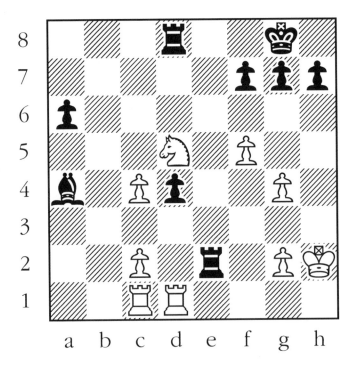

91.

White to move
(Deflection)

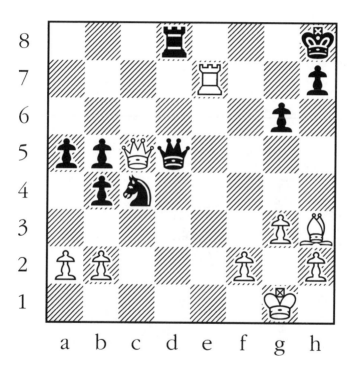

92.

White to move
(Mating attack)

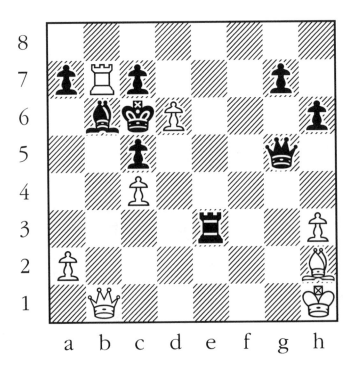

93.

White to move
(Deflection)

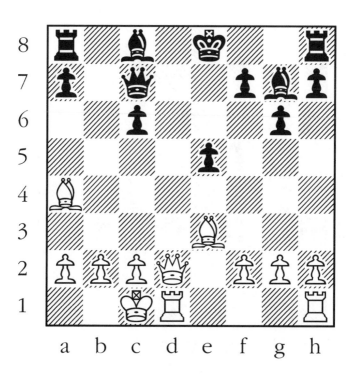

a b c d e f g h

94.

White to move
(Double threat)

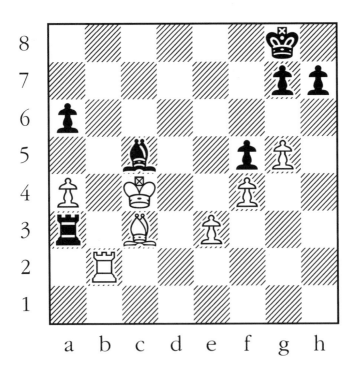

95.

White to move
(Pin)

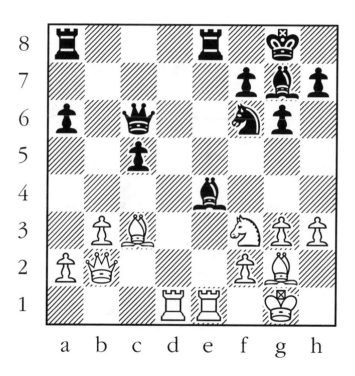

96.

White to move
(Removing the guard)

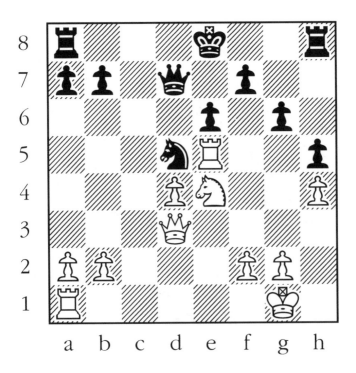

97.
Black to move
(Pin)

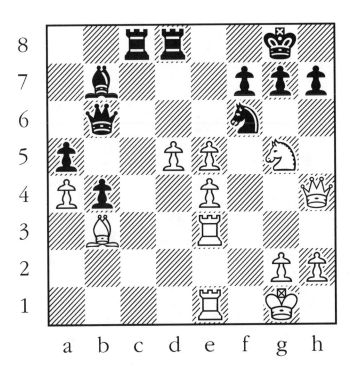

98.

Black to move
(Driving off)

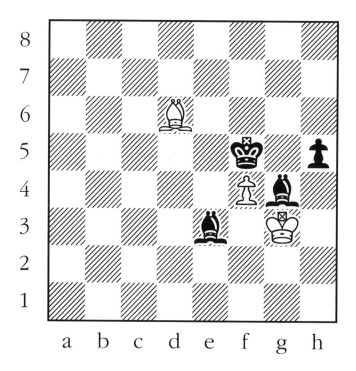

99.

Black to move
(Pin)

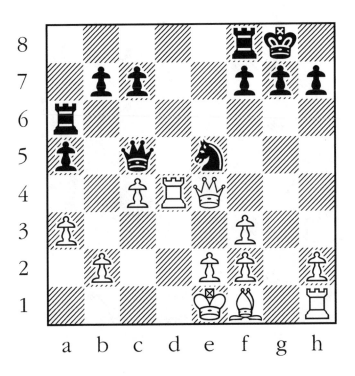

100.

Black to move
(Knight fork)

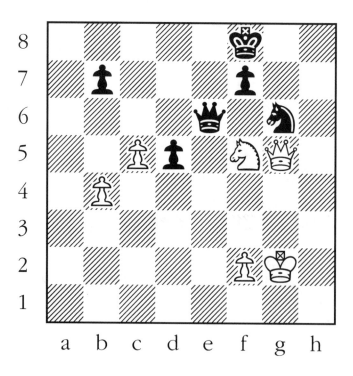

Bonus 1.
Black to move
(Removing the guard)

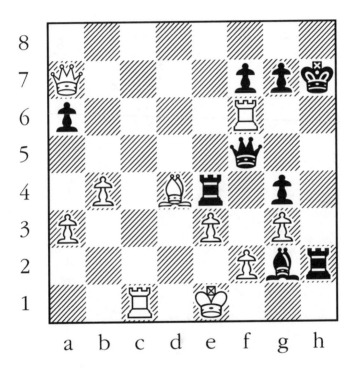

Bonus 2.

Black to move
(Driving off)

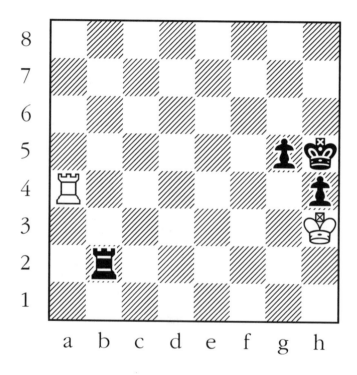

Bonus 3
White to move
(Skewer)

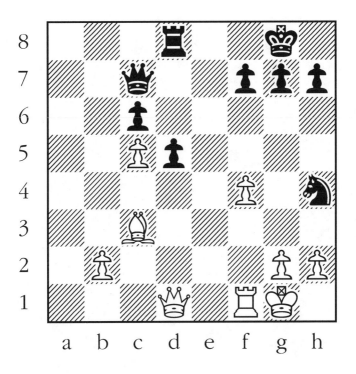

Bonus 4
White to move
(Skewer)

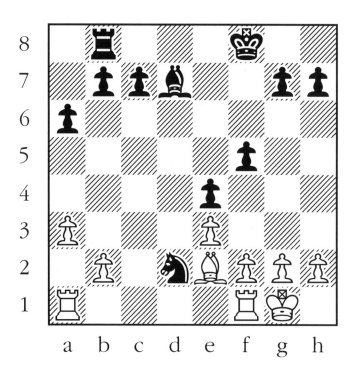

Bonus 5
White to move
(Mating attack)

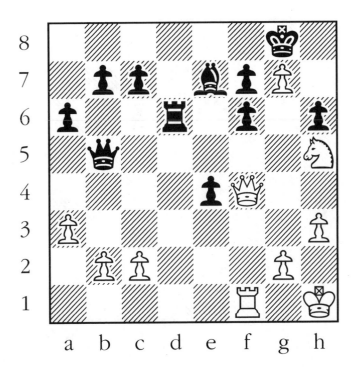

Bonus 6
White to move
(Discovery)

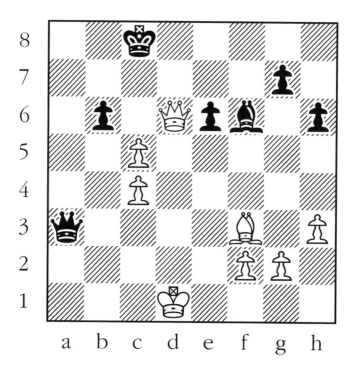

DEFENSE

D.

Black to move

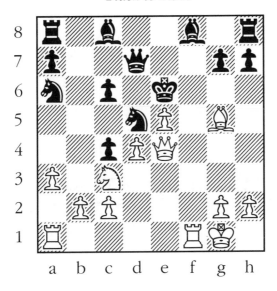

This section touches on a common theme that is rarely discussed in the literature of the game. What do you do in a rotten position? Miserable positions occur all the time. It happens to somebody in every decisive game. But the subject is too unpleasant, so nobody deals with it. It is much more handy to show how to win a won game than it is to show how to lose a lost one.

In the diagram position, it is Black to play and you can quickly discount his two extra pieces. The player's king is terribly exposed and it's about to get mated with Qf5# or Qg4#. Whatever hopes Black may have had about winning with extra material go by the wayside, since the immediate concern is to save the king. In this respect, however, Black's problem has become somewhat simplified. First fend off the impending mate, then worry about the resulting position later.

So the job at hand is to hold off checkmate. It is not so easy to do, but if you can find more than one way to do it, so much the better; then you can compare them. Of course, even then, there's no guarantee that you can save the game. But no matter. The primary defensive function is that of resistance. Salvation is a secondary concern.

A little studying of the board reveals that Black's only hope is to move his d5-knight. But where? The knight has eight possible squares. Three can be eliminated on sight, b4, b6, c7; all allow mate in one. And 1 … Ne7 is mate in two after 2 Qg4+ Nf5, 3 Qxf5#. That leaves four squares to look at.

Line One

1   …   Nxc3

Black removes the white knight and vacates the d5-square for his king. Unfortunately, White has a ready answer.

D1

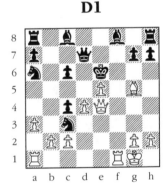

2   d5+!

Seals off the d5-square.

2   …   Nxd5

3   Qf5#

This is what happened in the actual game.

Line Two

1	...	**Nf6**	**D2**

Looking to shelter the king on the king-side, under cover of the knight.

2   exf6+

The shelter is quickly destroyed.

2	...	**Kf7**
3	**fxg7+**	**Kxg7**
4	**Bh6+!**	

Also winning is 4 Qe5+ or 4 Bf6+, but it turns out that White can go directly for mate.

4	...	**Kxh6**
5	**Qh4+**	**Kg6**
6	**Rf6+**	**Kg7**
7	**Qh6+**	**Kg8**
8	**Rxf8#**	

Mate allows us to draw the curtain on Line Two.

Line Three

1 ... Ne3 **D3**

The knight moves forward, guarding the squares f5 and g4. Of course the knight is en prise and can be captured in either of two ways. But Black's intention is to buy a little time.

2 Qxe3

Capture with the bishop, 2 Bxe3, gives Black time to withdraw his king, 2 ... Ke7 and 3 ... Ke8. By taking with the queen, White holds the black king in the center while threatening a new mate at h3.

2 ... Qxd4!

Black's defensive idea. The White queen is pinned and cannot get to h3.

3 Qxd4 Bc5

This second pin recovers the queen. And with the disappearance of the queens, White's immediate mating threats also vanish.

D4

True, to get to this position, Black has had to return all of his extra material, and he still stands very badly. But he's done all that he can reasonably be expected to do.

We've tested this position in training exercises and the results have been more or less what we expected. Masters have no trouble putting Black away. But below the Master level, Black escapes with a draw more often than not. And in a couple of instances Black even won!

However, our interest in Black has by now considerably diminished. He's already given his best shot. In the analysis that follows we seek to determine White's most efficient winning method.

4   Rd1

Threatens 5 Qxc5 Nxc5, 6 Rd6+ Kxe5, 7 Bf4+ Kf5, 8 Be3+ Ke5, 9 Bxc5. Black has no choice. He has to take the queen right away.

4	...	**Bxd4+**
5	**Rxd4**	

Now there's a new mating threat by 6 Rd6+ Kxe5, 7 Bf4+ Kf5, 8 h3 h5, 9 Bg3+ Kg5, 10 Ne4#. Again, Black has no choice but to boldly take the e5-pawn.

5	...	**Kxe5**
6	**Re4+**	**D5**

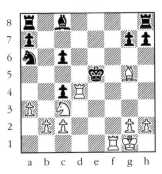

Despite the apparent danger, there seems no way for White to mate the black king in the center. Hence, White changes tack, driving Black's king to the edge.

6	...	**Kd6**
7	**Bf4+**	**Kc5**
8	**Be3+**	**Kd6**
9	**Rd1+**	**Kc7**
10	**Re7+**	**Kb8**
11	**Bf4+**	

Here, Black can safely resign with a clear conscience.

One bit of tidying up. Earlier, after 1 ... Ne3, we skipped over 2 Bxe3 because it allows Black's king to drop back by 2 ... Ke7. But White can also play this way. After 3 d5, he has a formidable attack for his sacrificed piece. We suspect it's a winning attack. It's just that it is more complicated. There are more pieces on the board and there are more ways to go wrong.

Line Four

1	...	**Nf4**	**D6**

The last of the black knight moves, offering itself up at f4 to block access to f5 and g4. White can of course play 2 Qxf4 when 2 ... Qxd4+ leads to lines already looked at. But White has something even better.

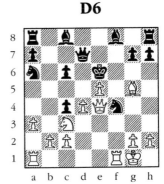

2   d5+!

The sealing move that we already encountered in Line One. Here it works to close down the d-file, preventing ... Qd4+. White will take the knight on his next move.

2   ...   cxd5

Naturally, 2 ... Kf7 is met by 3 e6+ forking king and queen.

3	**Qxf4**	**Bc5+**
4	**Kh1**	**Rf8**
5	**Qg4+**	**Kxe5**
6	**Qg3+!**	**Ke6**

On 6 … Kd4 White has a choice of four different mates in one.

7	**Rae1+**	**Be3**
8	**Rxe3#**	

Conclusion

The starting position (D) is lost for Black, but that's not too surprising. A position that looks lost generally is lost. Still, it is not yet time for Black to pack it in and resign. Resistance is still possible, through 1 ... Ne3. And while it is a thankless task it is not yet a hopeless task, as we discovered in the non-Master training games.

The defender's role is to defend. Keep looking. Keep fighting. Place whatever obstacles you can on the road to victory. Only then does salvation even become possible.

To complete the chapter we give the complete game score with comments by the winner.

B. Alberston vs. G. Besses
Allentown 1960
Two Knights Defense

1	e4	e5
2	Nf3	Nc6
3	Bc4	Nf6
4	Ng5	d5
5	exd5	Nxd5(?)

This natural recapture is thought to be a mistake. Theory recommends turning the opening into a gambit by 5 … Na5, or 5 … Nd4, or 5 … b5.

D7

6   Nxf7

The sacrifice of the knight is known as the Fried Liver Attack. It forces Black's king into the middle where it can be further attacked. Also pretty strong is 6 d4.

6   …   Kxf7

7   Qf3+   Ke6

The king comes up to protect the d5-knight. There have also been games where the king dropped back to e8. The typical conclusion was 7 … Ke8?, 8 Bxd5 Nd4?, 9 Qf7#. The four-move checkmate in nine moves.

8   Nc3   Ncb4

9   Qe4

Another line here is 9 a3 Nxc2+, 10 Kd1 and now Black is advised not to take the rook but to play 10 … Nd4.

9	…	c6
10	a3	Na6
11	d4	
11	…	Qd6?

D8

This is a serious error. Trying to hang on to the e5-pawn cannot be done. In attempting the impossible, Black loses precious time with his queen. Correct is 11 … Nc7, reinforcing the d5-square. Then Black has good chances to defend his position.

12	f4	b5
13	fxe5	Qd7
14	0-0	bxc4
15	Bg5	

And so the position is reached that began the chapter, Diagram 301. The finish was short and sweet.

D9

15	...	**Nxc3?**
16	**d5+!**	**Nxd5**
17	**Qf5#**	

Final Position

D10

Postscript

The 1960 game with Besses was played at a fast time (five or ten minutes). It was never recorded and quickly forgotten. Many years later, in the mid 1980s, I had to give a lesson on the Fried Liver Attack. I wanted an example that was short and crisp, and ended in mate. That's when the game with Besses came back to me. I had conducted it blindfold so it was still tucked away deep in my memory cells. All I had to do was retrieve it from my own head.

Only one thing bothered me. The game went like clockwork. My experience over the intervening 25 years had taught me that chess games don't really go that smoothly. Invariably, there are bumps in the road that pop up and slow down the mechanism. So, out came the board and the pieces, and then it was that 15 … Ne3 was uncovered.

As for the chess lesson, that did go like clockwork. And no, I did not mention Black's hidden resource. The trick in teaching is to know when to delete.

—Bruce Alberston

ANSWERS

1.

1 Qxf5 clips a pawn. The g6-pawn is pinned.

2.

After 1 Nc6 the black queen has no place to go.

3.

1 Bb3 pins and wins the black queen.

4.

1 ... Qd5+, 2 Kg1 Qxd1+ picks off the loose bishop.

5.

1 Rg4 wins the queen.

6.

1 ... Qxg3 wins a knight as the f2-pawn is pinned. White's last move was the careless 1 h3?.

7.

1 ... Be6 wins the exchange.

8.

1 Qa5 threatens 2 Qxc7# and 2 Qxh5. There's no defense to both.

9.

1 Nc2 catches the queen.

10.

1 … Rd4+, 2 Kg5 (not 2 Kxh5 Rxf5#) 2 … Nf6! (threatens 3 … h6#), 3 f4 Ne4+ forking king and queen.

11.

1 Rxc7 followed by 2 Rxe8 leaves White a full piece up.

12.

1 Rxe8+ and 2 Qxf7#.

13.

1 … Bc2 sets up two threats: 2 … Bxd1 and mostly 2 … g5#. There's no defense.

14.

The only way to stop the b-pawn is to stop the game. 1 … Re1+, 2 Rxe1 stalemate stops the game.

15.

1 … Nb5 cuts the queen's line of retreat. And 2 … Ra7 snares the queen. White can not prevent it.

16.

1 … Qe5+, 2 Qxe5 is stalemate.

17.

1 Rxd6+ along with 2 Rxb8 wins a full rook.

18.

White completes the mating net with 1 Na4 and 2 Nc3# (or 2 Nb6#).

19.

A rook down, Black escapes defeat by 1 … Rb8, 2 Rxb8 stalemate.

20.

1 Qf6 and queen mates at e7 or d8.

21.

1 … Nc1 wins either the exchange or the d3-bishop.

22.

1 Nd3 wins the exchange.

23.

1 Be4 and Black loses his rook in the corner after 1 …
Qxb7, 2 Bxb7.

24.

While 1 … Rxb5, 2 Nxg5 Bxb2 wins a pawn, 1 …
Bd4+! followed by 2 … Bxa7 wins a full piece!

25.

Black loses his bishop after 1 b3 and 2 Kb2.

26.

1 Rxe6+ fxe6, 2 Qe7#.

27.

White has an extra rook. Black has a check and the
attack. 1 Qf5! puts an end to both, 1 … gxf5, 2 Rd8#.

28.

Black to play forces the exchange of queens by 1 ... Qb3+. This kills White's attack and leaves Black a rook up.

29.

1 ... Rxd1, 2 Rxd1 Qxf6 wins a piece.

30.

1 ... Bxf2 wins at least the exchange, 2 Rg3 Bxg3. If 2 Bxf2 Rxh3.

31.

1 Bxe6+ picks up the exchange after 1 ... Nxe6, 2 Qxd5.

32.

1 Nf4 traps the queen.

33.

1 ... Rxd2+, 2 Rxd2 Rxe1 and Black should win the rook and pawn ending.

34.

1 Rxg7 Qxg7, 2 Qxh6 wins a piece.

35.

1 ... Bd8, 2 Qa7 Re7 and the queen is lost.

36.

1 ... Nf3+, 2 Rxf3 (else 2 ... Nxh4) 2 ... Bxf3 leaves Black ahead a piece for a pawn.

37.

1 Qc4+ Kxc4, 2 Ne3#.

38.

1 Bxh7+ Kxh7, 2 Qxf8.

39.

1 f4 Q-moves, 2 Qxd6.

40.

1 ... Ne3+ wins the queen. If 2 fxe3 Rg1#.

41.

1 ... Bxb3, 2 cxb3 Rxd3 wins a pawn.

42.

1 Nb6 Rd8, 2 Qxf7+ winning a pawn and breaking in.

43.

1 Rc8+ Nxc8, 2 Nc7#.

44.

1 Nf6+ wins the queen since 1 … gxf6, 2 Qg8#.

45.

1 … g3, 2 Bxg3 (else 2 … Rh2#) 2 … Rxg3 and mate in two more moves: 3 Kh2 Kf2, 4 Kh1 Rh3#.

46.

1 Rxa8 and if 1 … Rxa8, 2 Kxe3.

47.

1 … Rxe1+, 2 Kxe1 Qe2#.

48.

1 Rb7 Be8 (or 1 … Bg8), 2 f7 wins the bishop.

49.

1 Nd6+ Bxd6, 2 Nxe4 wins the queen.

50.

1 Bg5+ Kh7, 2 Rxc1.

51.

1 Bxe5 Nxe5, 2 Rxd4 gains a pawn.

52.

1 ... Rc5+, 2 Rxc5 b1/Q.

53.

1 ... Nf3+ and White must yield the exchange: 2 Rxf3 Rxf3.

54.

1 ... Bg4, 2 Qd2 Be2+ and White must give up the queen to save the king.

55.

1 Bxe6 wins a pawn. If 1 ... fxe6?, 2 Nxe6+ forks king and queen.

56.

1 Re7+ Kxe7, 2 h7 and promotes.

57.

1 Nc6 Rf8, 2 Ra1 traps the queen.

58.

1 Ne4 Q-moves, 2 Qxe3 wins the exchange.

59.

1 Rxb5 axb5, 2 cxb5 and the pawns are unstoppable.

60.

1 Rxd7 Qxd7, 2 Bb5 gains the queen.

61.

1 ... Bxe2, 2 Qxe2 Ng3#.

62.

1 ... Rxe3, 2 Rxe3 Bxd4 getting two pieces for the rook.

63.

1 Rg6+ fxg6, 2 Ng4#.

64.

1 Rh1+ Bxh1, 2 Rxh1#.

65.

1 Rf7+ Kh8, 2 Rf5 with Rh5# coming up.

66.

1 … Bh4, 2 g5 Bxf2+ wins the exchange. If White tries to save the rook, 2 Rg2, he loses his knight to 2 … f6.

67.

1 Rd7 wins the b7-bishop since 1 … Qxd7 runs into 2 Qxf6 and mate on g7.

68.

1 Qxh7+ Kxh7, 2 Kg2#.

69.

Simplest is 1 Qe5 f6, 2 Qxe6+. Also, 1 Bxg6 works:
1 … fxg6 (1 … hxg6?, 2 Rh8#), 2 Qxe6+ Rf7, 3 Rxh7
or 3 Qxg6+ and White is winning.

70.

1 Nxd5 Nxd5, 2 Rxc8+ wins a pawn.

71.

1 Qxd5 Qxd5, 2 Re8#.

72.

1 Qxh7+ Kxh7, 2 Rh6#.

73.

1 e6 fxe6 (or 1 … Qxe6), 2 Rxf5 wins a piece.

74.

1 … Kf3, 2 Rxe8 (what else?) 2 … g2#.

75.

1 Ne6+ wins the queen.

76.

1 … Rf5, 2 Qe2 Nxd4.

77.

1 … Rxf2 threatens 2 … Qxg2#. If 2 Qxf2 (or 2 Kxf2), then 2 … Bc5(+) pins or forks.

78.

1 … Rxe1+, 2 Bxe1 Bc5+, etc.

79.

1 Rg8+ Kxg8, 2 Qxf6.

80.

1 Bxg5 wins a pawn. If 1 … gxf5? then 2 f6+ discovers on the queen.

81.

1 Rxa5 bxa5, 2 Bxa7 wins a piece.

82.

1 Rd1 and if Black tries to save his pinned bishop with 1 … Ra7? he runs into a knight fork, 2 Nc6+ and 3 Nxa7.

83.

1 Qxg7 Bxg7, 2 e7 and promotes.

84.

1 Bc4 Bxc4, 2 bxc4 Kxc4, 3 g7 and promotes.

85.

1 Bxd5+ (A) 1 … Nxd5, 2 Qxg7# (B) 1 … Qxd5, 2 Qxc8+ and mates in two.

86.

1 e7 wins on the spot. If 1 … Qxg6, 2 exd8/Q+ and if the rook moves, then 2 e8/Q+.

87.

White is one move away from trapping Black's queen with 1 Nd2. Black to play, untraps by 1 … c4!, (A) 2 Qxc4 Qb2 or (B) 2 Qa4 b3.

88.

1 … Nc5, (A) 2 Qxa7 Ra8 (B) 2 Qb4 a5.

89.

1 Qxf6+ Rg7, 2 Qxg7#. Or 1 … Qxf6, 2 Rxh7#.

90.

1 Nc3 dxc3, 2 Rxd8+ wins the exchange. If 1 … Rxc2 then 2 Nxa4 wins a piece.

91.

1 Re8+ (A) 1 … Rxe8, 2 Qxd5 (B) 1 … Kg7, 2 Qf8#.

92.

1 Rxc7+ Bxc7, 2 Qb5# White can also start with 1 Qxb6+ but it takes a bit longer.

93.

1 Bxc6+ Ke7 (1 … Qxc6, 2 Qd8#), 2 Bxa8.

94.

1 Rb8+ Kf7 (1 … Bf8, 2 Bb4), 2 Bb2 wins the exchange.

95.

1 Rxe4 Rxe4 (1 … Nxe4, 2 Bxg7 or 1 … Qxe4, 2 Bxf6), 2 Ng5 wins material. There are too many pins and too many black pieces attacked.

96.

1 Rxd5 exd5 (or 1 … Qxd5), 2 Nf6+ forks king and queen.

97.

1 … Rc1 (threatens 2 … Qxe3+), 2 Qf2 (2 Rxc1 Qxe3+ and 3 … Qxc1+) 2 … Ng4 wins.

98.

1 … h4+, 2 Kg2 (2 Kxh4 Bf2#) 2 … Bxf4 and wins the ending.

99.

1 … Nxf3+, 2 exf3 (2 Qxf3 Qxd4) 2 … Re6 pins and wins the queen for rook and minor piece.

100.

1 … Qxf5, 2 Qxf5 Nh4+ and 3 … Nxf5 winning a piece.

Bonus 1.

Not 1 … gxf6?, 2 Qxf7+. First 1 … Rh1+, 2 Kd2 Rxd4+, 3 Qxd4 and only now 3 … gxf6 winning.

Bonus 2.

1 … g4+, 2 Rxg4 Rb3+, 3 Kg2 Kxg4 picking up a rook.

Bonus 3.

1 Qe1 Nf5, 2 Ba5 Q-moves 3 Bxd8 wins the exchange.

Bonus 4.

1 Rad1 (better than 1Rfd1 Nb3) 1 … Nxf1, 2 Rxd7 followed by taking the knight.

Bonus 5.

1 Qxh6 Qxf1+, 2 Kh2 and Qh8# is unstoppable.

Bonus 6.

1 Bb7+ Kxb7, 2 c6+ and 3 Qxa3.

Index

WHAT IS MENSA?

Mensa—The High IQ Society

Mensa is the international society for people with a high IQ. We have more than 100,000 members in over 40 countries worldwide.

The society's aims are:
- to identify and foster human intelligence for the benefit of humanity;
- to encourage research in the nature, characteristics, and uses of intelligence;
- to provide a stimulating intellectual and social environment for its members.

Anyone with an IQ score in the top two percent of the population is eligible to become a member of Mensa—are you the "one in 50" we've been looking for?

Mensa membership offers an excellent range of benefits:
- Networking and social activities nationally and around the world;
- Special Interest Groups (hundreds of chances to pursue your hobbies and interests—from art to zoology!);
- Monthly International Journal, national magazines, and regional newsletters;
- Local meetings—from game challenges to food and drink;
- National and international weekend gatherings and conferences;
- Intellectually stimulating lectures and seminars;
- Access to the worldwide SIGHT network for travelers and hosts.

For more information about Mensa International:

www.mensa.org
Mensa International
15 The Ivories
6–8 Northampton Street
Islington, London N1 2HY
United Kingdom

For more information about American Mensa:

www.us.mensa.org
Telephone: (800) 66-MENSA
American Mensa Ltd.
1229 Corporate Drive West
Arlington, TX 76006-6103 US

For more information about British Mensa (UK and Ireland):

www.mensa.org.uk
Telephone: +44 (0) 1902 772771
E-mail: enquiries@mensa.org.uk
British Mensa Ltd.
St. John's House
St. John's Square
Wolverhampton WV2 4AH
United Kingdom